Usborne

Little Coloring
Animals

Illustrated by Jenny Brown

Words by Kirsteen Robson

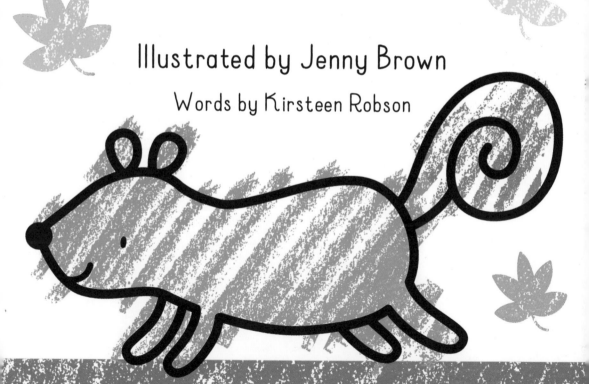

An elephant
and her baby

A wide-awake owl

A hissing
snake

A swimming
turtle

A purring cat

A hen with her chicks

A diving
dolphin

A furry
fox

A swooping
bat

A fluffy rabbit

A clinging chameleon

A little
bird

A fancy fish

A swinging
monkey

A muddy
piglet

A watchful
meerkat

A prancing
llama

A squeaking mouse

Happy
Lions

A gentle
seahorse

A climbing
koala

A duck
and her
ducklings

A big
bear

A playful
penguin

A perching parrot

A cheerful horse

A smiling squirrel

A friendly dog

A tall
flamingo

A sleepy
sloth

Pretty butterflies